MW00826629

Tea Party
Coloring Book

CREATIVE COLORING PRESS

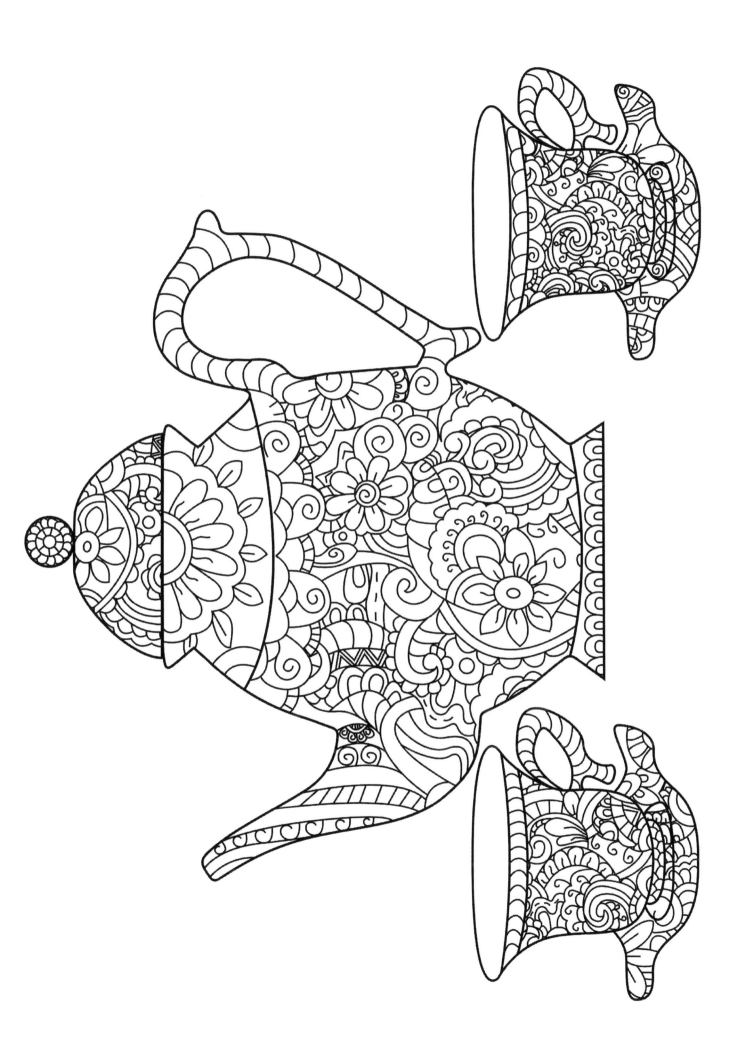

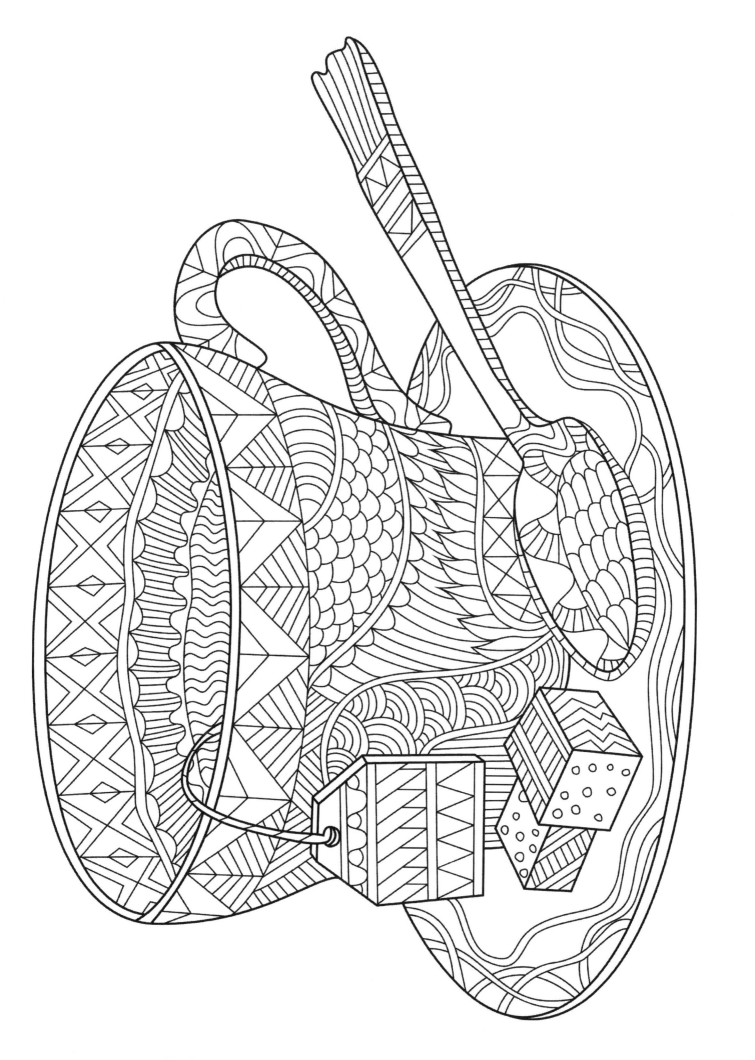

Thank you for purchasing this coloring book! I hope that you enjoy coloring it as much as we enjoyed creating it. Please consider leaving a review, we really appreciate hearing your opinion!

Sign-Up to Get a Free Coloring Book

Subscribe to our newsletter and get a free printable coloring book of some of our most popular illustrations. Plus you'll receive special offers, sneak peeks at new releases, and more.
Visit us at **www.creativecoloring.co** for details.

We want to hear from you!

We hope you've enjoyed this coloring book and that is brings you many hours of fun, stress relief, and creativity. We'd love to see and share your creations.

Send us your ideas, suggestions, and finished artwork:

www.creativecoloring.co
facebook.com/creativecoloringpress
Instagram: @creativecoloringpress
Twitter: @creativecoloringpress

Bonus

Turn the page for bonus pages from some of our most popular coloring books.

Cat Coloring Book

An Adult Coloring Book for Cat Lovers

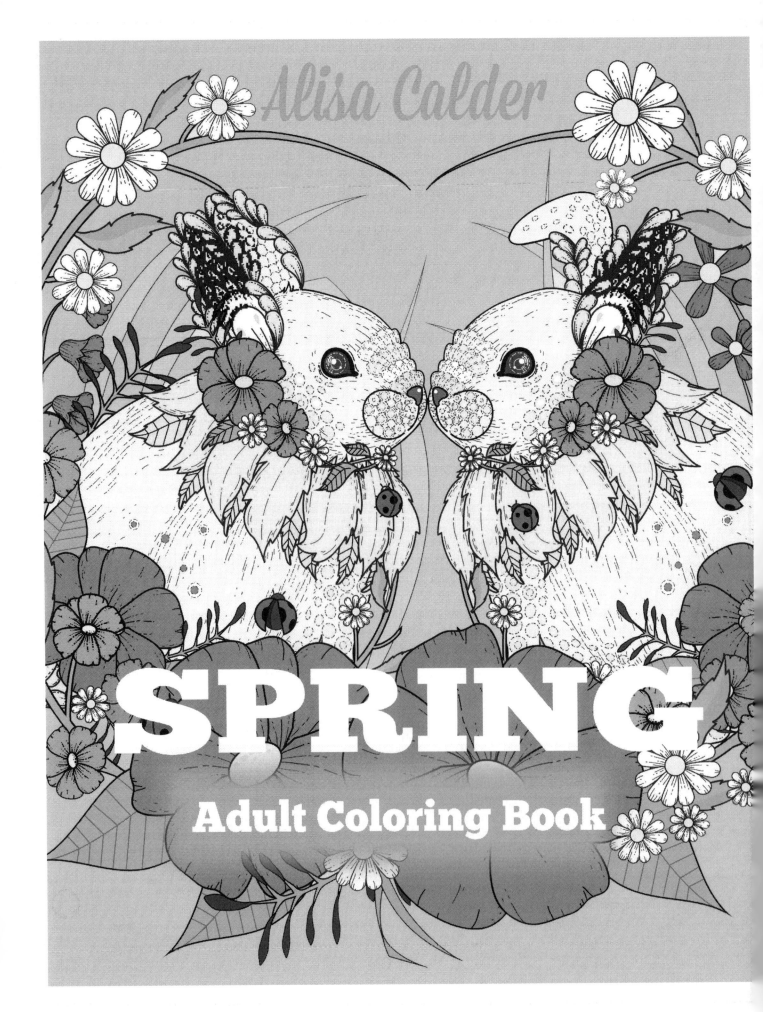

CREATIVE COLORING PRESS

LIFE UNDER THE SEA

COLORING BOOK FOR ADULTS

An
Ocean
Coloring
Adventure

Fabulous FOOD
Coloring Book

Creative Coloring

Copyright © 2018 by Creative Coloring Press
All rights reserved.

69340718R00049

Made in the USA
Middletown, DE
19 September 2019